July, 2020

To: Corinne (Coco)

I hope you enjoy this book!
What are your wonderful things?
Love,
Val Lowrey Doherty

First Published in 2020 by Blossom Spring Publishing

Wonderful Things © 2020 Valerie Doherty

ISBN 978-1-8380982-0-9

E: admin@blossomspringpublishing.com
W: www.blossomspringpublishing.com

Wonderful Things

by Valerie Doherty

Illustrated by Brenda Higgins

For my parents.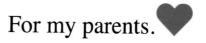

Read Aloud Benefits
for the Youngest Listeners:

1. Per recent early childhood researchers, the read aloud bedtime story is one of the most powerful rituals between child and caregiver.

2. Story time establishes a connection between child and the reader.

3. Children hear a comforting and familiar voice.

4. Reading stimulates cognitive and language development.

5. Early shared book experiences with a loved one can establish a pattern of "book love" and reading pleasure across the life span.

So, create a comforting environment, cuddle up, and enjoy a book together before bedtime or nap!

Pink and blue skies
Birds and butterflies

Falling white snow

BREAD

Lullabyes sung low

Blue lakes for toes
New puppies
with bows

3

Picnics and bugs
Good friends
to share hugs

Sunlight
so bright

Twinkly stars,
moonlight

Mountains so tall
Color splash in fall

7

Springtime flowers
Thunder and showers

8

Beaches to run
   Happy days, big fun

A hand
to hold
A laugh,
big and
bold

10

Secrets to share
Nice people
who care

Rainbows and light

Warm covers
at night

Good things
to eat

New friends that we meet

Soft winds that blow

A bright, light-filled show

14

A lovely day

Sandcastles and play

Joy, you and me

Surprises
we see

16

Places to roam

A sweet place
called home

17

Wonderful
things

Every new day
brings

18

About the Author

Valerie Lowrey Doherty is a speech-language pathologist, early childhood educator, and author. She has professional interests in language and literacy development across the lifespan. She enjoys playing with words, creating stories, reading all kinds of books, and dancing.

She lives with her family and shares time between suburban Chicago and Nebraska. *Wonderful Things* is her fourth children's book publication.

Visit her website at *www.valeriedohertyauthor.com*.

About the Illustrator

Although born in Dublin, Ireland, Brenda has lived in Malaga, Spain for the last sixteen years. She has been illustrating children's literature during this time, and her work can be seen in America, Ireland, Spain, and Australia. Brenda enriches the text with vibrant color and images which enable children to "feel" the words with imagination.

Made in the USA
Monee, IL
23 July 2020